Power of 2

The one-to-one coaching system
for maths success

David J Sharp

Copies of this book can be obtained from 123 Learning
www.123learning.co.uk

Power of 2: The one-to-one coaching system for maths success
ISBN: 978-0-9539812-0-5

Published by Power of 2 Publishing, Nottingham, England.

First published 2001
Reprinted 2017
Printed in the UK

Also available from 123 Learning

Plus 1: The introductory coaching system for maths success
ISBN: 978-0-9539812-1-2

Perform with Time: The one-to-one coaching system for success with time
ISBN: 978-0-9539812-2-9

**Perform with Time Tables: The one-to-one coaching system for success
with multiplication and division**
ISBN: 978-0-9539812-3-6

This book belongs to: Finn

Acknowledgements

A big thank you to everyone who has helped
to develop Power of 2.

To colleagues at Fernwood Comprehensive School
for their useful feedback. To Chris Rhodes for initially
highlighting the need for such a book. To Anne Archer
for her help with the layout. To Trish and Gavin Tunstall
for their encouragement and ideas. To Jayne Lee for the
name 'Power of 2' and her enthusiasm for the book.
To Adrian Bhagat for the website. To Hugh Sharp for
proof-reading and casting a fresh eye over the book.
Finally, to Jan, for her support and belief in the 'Power of 2.'

Welcome to the Power of 2

Power of 2 is so called because of the proven success of 2 people working together. It stems from the need of some people to have more reinforcement and practice than is often available.

Part of the reason for the huge success of the Power of 2 is the immense sense of achievement that a person gets when working through the book. This feeling should not be underestimated and therefore this book must be seen as a whole programme of study. It is not intended that certain pages should be used in isolation. A contents page has not been included for this reason.

It is intended that everyone should start at the beginning and work through the whole book. Students will quickly find their own level. They will also gain a sense of success and confidence.

On each page there is a 'script' for the coach to read, or this could be read by the student. Write down the date you begin each page. There is a space in the bottom left hand corner for this. When each page is completed, record the date in the bottom right hand corner. Please see the worked examples on pages 10 and 11.

Power of 2 has been found to work best when it is used 4 or 5 times a week, with each session lasting for about 10 - 15 minutes. It is for this reason that we encourage you not to leave it too long between sessions.

Using this book

Three ticks

Power of 2 requires that each question is answered correctly on three consecutive occasions on different days. When a question is answered correctly, a tick should be placed on the line. If the question is not answered correctly, then a dot should be used instead. When a question has been given three consecutive ticks, that question need not be asked again. If a student has not gained three consecutive ticks for a particular question, by the end of the grid, then that question should be written in the next Recap grid.

Three consecutive ticks are also required on the Recap grid pages. Please see the worked example on pages 10 and 11.

Here are a few ideas that you may find useful when working through Power of 2.

Accepting the first answer

It is good for the coach to accept the first answer that is given. This will encourage students to think before answering and to find a suitable method to use. However self-correction by the student should be encouraged and therefore you should use your discretion when wrong answers are self-corrected.

Coaching and helping the student

If any coaching or help is given, do not tick the question on that day. If a wrong answer is offered, put a dot in the box next to the question. If any help is needed to enable the student to complete the calculation, a dot should also be placed next to that question.

Notes and working out

On each page there is space available for your notes and working out. This space can be used by both the coach and the student. Students will find diagrams very helpful to demonstrate different methods that can be used. There are separate pages of explanation throughout the book which you may find useful.

"How did you work that out?"

It's good to ask a student, "How did you work that out?". Firstly it can reinforce the method that the student uses. Secondly it can encourage students to use mathematical vocabulary. Also there are no answers in this book. Asking how an answer was worked out gives the student (and coach) an opportunity to check that the answer is correct.

The power of success

Part of the reason for the success of this book is the sense of achievement gained by the students as they work through the pages. Students will get a great deal of pride from seeing their progress. Setting targets for the student to reach by a certain date will also aid the sense of achievement. The power of success should not be underestimated. This feeling of achievement will be compounded when they see the pages being ticked off. It has been found that using an elastic band to hold the completed pages works well in showing the progress made.

Quick recall

Each student needs to increase the calculations they can do 'without thinking'. If they 'know' certain facts they can then concentrate on other aspects of their maths. Students need regular practice in these skills. Too often, students rely on their fingers and counting to do simple calculations. This will hinder their progress. Power of 2 allows students to get repeated practice in facts that they need to know to develop their maths. The book also gives a great deal of revision, which alongside the "three ticks" helps to develop learning.

Mental calculations

Power of 2 is essentially about mental calculations. Students should be encouraged to carry out the calculations in this book without using pen and paper. The explanation sheets throughout the book give examples of mental methods which can be used. It's good to encourage students to think of the best method for each question. Be aware that some written methods that students will use will be different to the principles used when they use mental methods.

Many mental methods are carried out from left to right, therefore starting with the most significant digits. Many written methods often work from right to left, and use each digit without recognising its value.

Written methods

The blank space in Power of 2 can be used by the coach to explain methods and remind students about strategies they can use. However, students may want to jot down some notes about their work. This might be jotting down their mid-way answers.

For example, 534 x 4

First they would jot down 1068 (534 x 2)
Then, by doubling, work out 2136 (1068 x 2)

Mathematical vocabulary

It's important that students know and can use the correct terminology. They need to be able to say "three hundred and forty six" and not just "three-four-six". Also they need to know that 1.25 is read as "one point two five" and not "one point twenty five". The coach should also emphasise links between connected terms. For example, that 'halving' is the same as 'dividing by 2'.

Games and activities

There is one game included in this book. The game (Sum to 15) is intended to show the student that maths can be used for enjoyment as well as necessity.

Adding 10

Add 10 to these numbers.

Say the number which is 10 more than...

For example,
4   You say "14"

You must earn three consecutive ticks.

4	/	·	·	/	/	/	
9	·	/	/	/			
7	/	/	·	/	/	/	
15	/	/	/				
3	/	/	/				
19	·	/	/	/			
1	·	·	·	·	/	/	/
22	·	·	/	·	/	/	·
46	·	/	/	/			
90	/	/	/				
58	/	/	·	/	/	/	
37	/	/	/				
6	·	·	/	/	/		

Use this space for your notes and working out.

example

Page 10 started on: 15/1/2017 _ _ _ _ _ _ _ _ _ _ _

Page 10 finished on: 24/1/2017 _ _ _ _ _ _ _ _ _ _ _

Recap grid

Use this space for your notes and working out.

Use this grid to put in any question you have found difficult so far.

You can put in the questions you found hard or you can make up your own.

You still need to get three consecutive ticks.

22 + 10	·	/	/	/			

Page 11 started on: 24/1/2017

Page 11 finished on: 28/1/2017

Reading numbers

Read these numbers aloud.

You must earn three consecutive ticks.

5								
21								
79								
92								
104								
60								
108								
240								
337								
1,000								
1,250								
2,003								
150								

Use this space for your notes and working out.

Page 12 started on: _ _ _ _ _ _ _ _ _ _ _ _ _

Page 12 finished on: _ _ _ _ _ _ _ _ _ _ _ _ _

Reading signs

Use this space for your notes and working out.

Read these signs aloud.

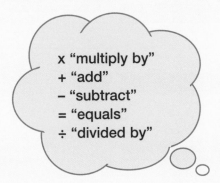

x "multiply by"
+ "add"
– "subtract"
= "equals"
÷ "divided by"

+							
–							
÷							
X							
=							
–							
X							
÷							
=							
+							
÷							
–							
=							

Number bonds to 10

It's really important that you know which numbers add up to 10.

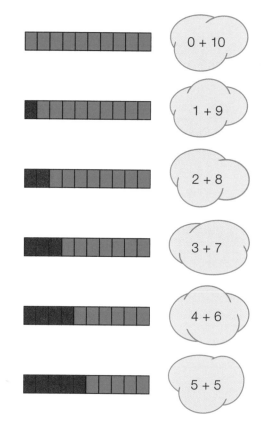

Use this space for your notes and working out.

Number bonds to 10

Use this space for your notes and working out.

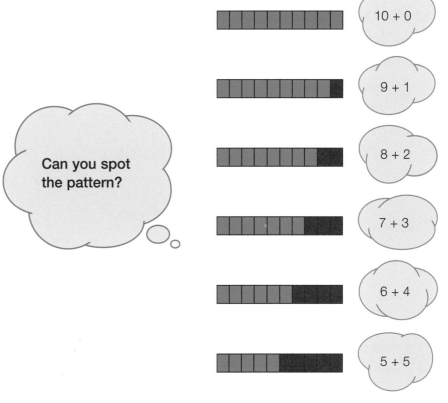

Can you spot the pattern?

10 + 0

9 + 1

8 + 2

7 + 3

6 + 4

5 + 5

Number bonds to 10

Read out the whole sum.

For example,

$2 + \square = 10$

Read out,
"Two add eight equals ten"

$2 + \boxed{8} = 10$

$4 + \boxed{6} = 10$	✓	✓	✓				
$9 + \boxed{1} = 10$	✓	✓	✓				
$2 + \boxed{8} = 10$	✓	✓	✓				
$6 + \boxed{4} = 10$	✓	✓	✓				
$3 + \boxed{7} = 10$	✓	✓	✓				
$5 + \boxed{5} = 10$	✓	✓	✓				
$7 + \boxed{3} = 10$	✓	✓	✓				
$1 + \boxed{9} = 10$	✓	✓	✓				
$10 + \boxed{0} = 10$	✓	✓	✓				
$4 + \boxed{6} = 10$	✓	✓	✓				
$8 + \boxed{2} = 10$	✓	✓	✓				
$3 + \boxed{7} = 10$	✓	✓	✓				
$0 + \boxed{10} = 10$	✓	✓	✓				

Use this space for your notes and working out.

Page 16 started on: _ _ _ _ May _ _ 11 2019

Page 16 finished on: _ May _ 16 2019

Adding one

Use this space for your notes and working out.

Say out loud the number which is one more than these numbers

For example,

6   You say "seven"

6	/	/	/				
8	/	/	/				
19	/	/	/				
30	/	/	/				
79	/	/	/				
100	/	/	/				
129	/	/	/				
89	/	/	/				
35	/	/	/				
99	·	/	/	/			
279	/	·	/	/	/		
599	/	/	/				
43	/	/	/				

Doubles

If you can double numbers, it will help you do many other things.

For example,

Double 8

$$8 = 5 + 3$$
$$\downarrow \text{Double} \downarrow$$
$$10 + 6 = 16$$

So double 8 is 16

One way to work out doubles is to split them up into numbers you can double

Double 7

$$7 = 5 + 2$$
$$\downarrow \text{Double} \downarrow$$
$$10 + 4 = 14$$

So double 7 is 14

Double 9

$$9 = 5 + 4$$
$$\downarrow \text{Double} \downarrow$$
$$10 + 8 = 18$$

So double 9 is 18

Doubles

Use this space for your notes and working out.

Say out loud the number that is double these numbers.

For example,
6   You should say,
       "Double six is twelve"

Don't forget that doubling numbers is the same as multiplying by 2

Look

6 x 2 = 12
Double 6 is 12

6	/	/			
3	/	/	/	/	
2	/	/			
5	/	/			
1	/	/			
4	/	/			
7	/	/			
5	/	/			
10	/	/			
9	/	/			
8	/	/			
7	/	/			
4	/	/			

More number bonds to 10

Read out the whole sum.

For example,
$$\square + 7 = 10$$

Read out,
"Three add seven equals ten"
$$\boxed{3} + 7 = 10$$

$\square + 7 = 10$	/	/	/				
$4 + \square = 10$	/	/	/				
$5 + \square = 10$	/	/	/				
$10 + \square = 10$	/	/	/				
$2 + \square = 10$	/	/	/				
$\square + 9 = 10$	/	/	/				
$8 + \square = 10$	/	/	/				
$0 + \square = 10$	/	/	/				
$\square + 3 = 10$	/	/	/				
$6 + \square = 10$	/	/	/				
$\square + 5 = 10$	/	/	/				
$7 + \square = 10$	/	/	/				
$\square + 4 = 10$	/	/	/				

Use this space for your notes and working out.

Page 20 started on: may 11 2019

Page 20 finished on: 18 2019 May

You can use this 100 square to help you add on 10.

For example,

28 + 10 = ☐

Look at the squares

28
38

Going down a square adds on 10

So   28 + 10 = 38

100 square

1	2	3	4	5	6	7	8	9	10
11	12	13	14	15	16	17	18	19	20
21	22	23	24	25	26	27	28	29	30
31	32	33	34	35	36	37	38	39	40
41	42	43	44	45	46	47	48	49	50
51	52	53	54	55	56	57	58	59	60
61	62	63	64	65	66	67	68	69	70
71	72	73	74	75	76	77	78	79	80
81	82	83	84	85	86	87	88	89	90
91	92	93	94	95	96	97	98	99	100

Adding 10

Add 10 to these numbers.

Say the number which is 10 more than...

For example,
4   You say "14"

You must earn three consecutive ticks.

> **You can use the 100 square on page 21 to help**

4	✓	✓	✓					
9	✓	✓	✓					
7	✓	✓	✓					
15	✓	✓	✓					
3	✓	✓	✓					
19	✓	✓	✓					
1	✓	✓	✓					
22	✓	✓	✓					
46	•	•	•	✓	✓	✓		
90	✓	✓	✓					
58	✓	✓	✓					
37	✓	✓	•	✓	✓	✓		
6	✓	✓	✓					

Use this space for your notes and working out

Page 22 started on: _May 11 2019_

Page 22 finished on: _3 July 2019_

Doubles

Use this space for your notes and working out.

Say the number that is double these numbers.

For example,

7   You should say "Double seven is fourteen"

Don't forget that doubling is the same as multiplying by 2.

Look

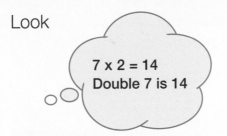

7 x 2 = 14
Double 7 is 14

7	✓	✓	✓			
10	✓	✓	✓			
9	✓	✓	✓			
6	✓	✓	✓			
8	✓	✓	✓			
11	✓	✓	✓			
14	✓	•	✓	✓		
5	✓	✓	✓			
3	✓	✓	✓			
12	✓	✓	✓			
1	✓	✓	✓			
20	✓	✓	✓			
7	✓	✓	✓			

Nearly numbers

Numbers near to a multiple of 10 can be called nearly numbers.

These are some nearly numbers

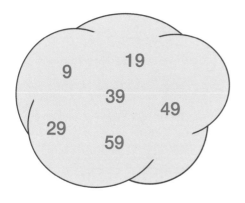

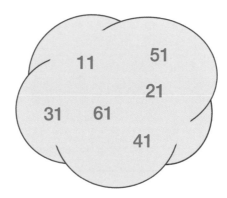

Nearly numbers

**You can use nearly numbers
to help you.**

For example,   6 + 9

First you can add 10, then subtract 1

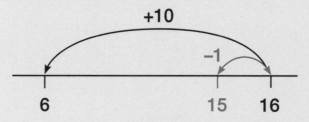

So,   6 + 9 = 15

Adding 9

A quick way to add 9 is to add 10 and then subtract 1.

So for example,

$5 + 9$ would be:

$5 + 10 = 15$
$15 - 1 = 14$

So, $5 + 9 = \boxed{14}$

Read out the whole sum and give the answer.

$5 + 9 =$ ☐	/	/	/					
$2 + 9 =$ ☐	/	/	/					
$8 + 9 =$ ☐	/	/	/					
$3 + 9 =$ ☐	/	/	/					
$1 + 9 =$ ☐	/	/	/					
$4 + 9 =$ ☐	/	/	/					
$7 + 9 =$ ☐	/	/	/					
$9 + 9 =$ ☐	/	/	/					
$9 + 6 =$ ☐	/	/	/					
$10 + 9 =$ ☐	/	/	/					
$8 + 9 =$ ☐	/	/	/					
$9 + 0 =$ ☐	/	/	/					
$6 + 9 =$ ☐	/	/	/					

Use this space for your notes and working out.

Addition and subtraction

Use this space for your notes and working out.

Addition and subtraction up to 10.

Read out the whole question.

Only your first answer will be accepted.

For example,

$$8 - 3 = \square$$

You say,
"8 take away 3 equals 5"

$$8 - 3 = \boxed{5}$$

$8 - 3 = \square$	•	•	•	/			
$4 + 5 = \square$	/	/	/				
$6 + 2 = \square$	/	/	/				
$9 - 3 = \square$	/	/	/				
$4 + 3 = \square$	/	/	/				
$1 + \square = 7$	/	/	/				
$10 - 6 = \square$	/	/	/				
$3 + \square = 8$	/	/	/				
$\square - 2 = 6$	/	/	/				
$7 - \square = 3$	/	/	/				
$\square - 2 = 7$	/	/	/				
$10 - \square = 0$	/	/	/				
$4 + 4 = \square$	/	/	/				

Recap grid

Use this grid to put in any question you have found difficult so far.

You can put in the questions you found hard or you can make up your own.

You still need to get three consecutive ticks.

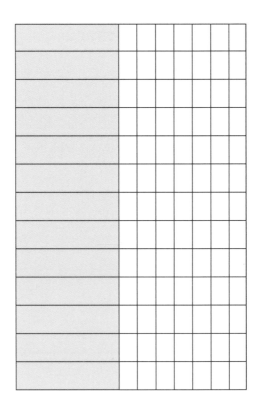

Use this space for your notes and working out.

Use this space for your notes and working out.

Read these numbers aloud.

You must get three consecutive ticks.

Read these signs.

8	✓	✓	✓				
14	✓	✓	✓				
2,036	✓	✓	✓				
403	✓	✓	✓				
3,800	✓	✓	✓				
105	✓	✓	✓				
1,902	✓	✓	✓				

÷	✓	✓	✓				
=	✓	✓	✓				
+	✓	✓	✓				
÷	✓	✓	✓				
−	✓	✓	✓				
=	✓	✓	✓				
x	✓	✓	✓				

Adding 1

Add 1 to these numbers.

Read out the answer.

You must earn three consecutive ticks.

Doubles

Double these numbers.

Read out the answer.

You must earn three consecutive ticks.

Use this space for your notes and working out.

16	✓	✓	✓					
29	✓	✓	✓					
74	✓	✓	✓					
104	✓	✓	✓					
149	✓	✓	✓					
45	?	✓	✓					
50	✓	✓	✓					

7	✓	✓	✓					
9	✓	✓	✓					
14	✓	✓	✓					
8	✓	✓	✓					
5	✓	✓	✓					
10	✓	✓	✓					
6	✓	✓	✓					

Page 30 started on: _14 May 2019_

Page 30 finished on: 3 July 2019

Number bonds to 10

Use this space for your notes and working out.

Read out the whole sum.

6 + ☐ = 10	/
3 + ☐ = 10	/
5 + ☐ = 10	/
7 + ☐ = 10	/
9 + ☐ = 10	/
10+ ☐ = 10	/
2 + ☐ = 10	/

☐ + 5 = 10	/
9 + ☐ = 10	/
☐ + 8 = 10	/
3 + ☐ = 10	/
6 + ☐ = 10	/
☐ + 1 = 10	/
☐ + 4 = 10	/

Page 31 started on: _22 May 2019_

Page 31 finished on: _ _ _ _ _ _ _ _ _ _ _ _ _

Subtraction from 10

You can use your number bonds to 10 to help you with subtraction.

For example,

$$10 - \square = 3$$

Remember these pairs that add up to 10.

0 and 10

1 and 9

2 and 8

3 and 7

4 and 6

5 and 5

← So it must be $10 - \boxed{7} = 3$

Subtracting from 10

Use this space for your notes and working out.

Read out the whole sum.

So for example,

$$10 - \square = 3$$

You say "Ten take away seven equals three"

$$10 - \boxed{7} = 3$$

You must earn three consecutive ticks.

$10 - \square = 3$	✓						
$10 - \square = 9$	✓						
$10 - 4 = \square$	✓						
$10 - \square = 7$	✓						
$10 - 6 = \square$	✓						
$10 - \square = 10$	✓						
$10 - 2 = \square$	°						
$10 - \square = 1$	✓						
$10 - \square = 5$	✓						
$10 - 8 = \square$	✓						
$10 - 3 = \square$	✓						
$10 - \square = 9$	✓						
$10 - \square = 2$	✓						

Doubles

Say the number that is double these numbers.

For example,
3   You should say,

"Double three is six"

Don't forget that doubling numbers is the same as multiplying by 2.

Look

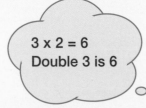

3 x 2 = 6
Double 3 is 6

3								
11								
13								
10								
8								
15								
12								
16								
7								
19								
6								
9								
4								

Use this space for your notes and working out.

Adding 11

Use this space for your notes and working out.

A quick way to add 11 is to add 10 and then add an extra 1.

So for example,

5 + 11 would be:

5 + 10 = 15
15 + 1 = 16

So,   5 + 11 = $\boxed{16}$

Read out the whole sum and give the answer.

Remember "Nearly numbers"

5 + 11 = ☐							
2 + 11 = ☐							
18 + 11 = ☐							
23 + 11 = ☐							
11 + 16 = ☐							
11 + 9 = ☐							
37 + 11 = ☐							
11 + 51 = ☐							
6 + 11 = ☐							
74 + 11 = ☐							
8 + 11 = ☐							
11 + 0 = ☐							
15 + 11 = ☐							

Pick 'n' mix to 10

Read out the whole sum.

So for example,

$$10 - \square = 3$$

You say "Ten take away seven equals three"

$$10 - \boxed{7} = 3$$

You must earn three consecutive ticks.

$10 - \square = 3$							
$8 + \square = 10$							
$\square + 1 = 10$							
$10 - \square = 6$							
$10 - 5 = \square$							
$\square + 4 = 10$							
$8 + \square = 10$							
$\square + 7 = 10$							
$2 + \square = 10$							
$10 - \square = 4$							
$10 - \square = 0$							
$3 + \square = 10$							
$10 - \square = 9$							

Use this space for your notes and working out.

Adding 9

Use this space for your notes and working out.

A quick way to add 9, is to add 10 and then take away 1.

So for example,

$43 + 9$ would be

$43 + 10 = 53$
$53 - 1 = 52$

So, $43 + 9 = \boxed{52}$

Read out the whole sum and give the answer.

$43 + 9 = \square$	
$26 + 9 = \square$	
$87 + 9 = \square$	
$23 + 9 = \square$	
$19 + 9 = \square$	
$9 + 82 = \square$	
$78 + 9 = \square$	
$49 + 9 = \square$	
$9 + 95 = \square$	
$104 + 9 = \square$	
$9 + 65 = \square$	
$120 + 9 = \square$	
$33 + 9 = \square$	

Halving

Say the number that is half of these numbers.

For example,
12   You should say,
      "Half of 12 is 6"

Don't forget that halving is the same as dividing by 2.

Look

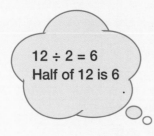

12 ÷ 2 = 6
Half of 12 is 6

12								
8								
10								
6								
16								
4								
18								
14								
20								
16								
24								
16								
2								

Use this space for your notes and working out.

Adding 20

You can use the 100 square on page 21 to help you

Use this space for your notes and working out.

Add 20 to these numbers.

Read the number that is 20 more than...

For example,

34   You say "54"

34 + 20 = $\boxed{54}$

You must earn three consecutive ticks.

34							
12							
5							
15							
20							
7							
27							
53							
31							
14							
28							
72							
37							

More doubles

Remember that you can
split numbers up to help
you double numbers.

Double 17, $17 = 10 + 7$

$\downarrow$ Double $\downarrow$

$20 + 14 = 34$

So double 17 is 34

You can also split the
numbers up in other ways.

Double 18, $18 = 10 + 5 + 3$

$\downarrow$ Double $\downarrow$ Double $\downarrow$

$20 + 10 + 6 = 36$

So double 18 is 36

More doubles

Use this space for your notes and working out.

Say the number that is double these numbers.

For example,

12   You should say, "Double twelve is twenty four"

Don't forget that doubling numbers is the same as multiplying by 2.

Look

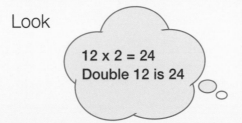

12 x 2 = 24
Double 12 is 24

12						
15						
7						
13						
17						
19						
11						
8						
18						
10						
9						
16						
14						

Subtraction from 10

Doubles

Read out the whole sum.

Read out the whole sum.

Use this space for your notes and working out.

10 – 2 = ☐	
10 – ☐ = 7	
10 – 5 = ☐	
10 – ☐ = 10	
10 – 9 = ☐	
10 – ☐ = 4	
10 – 8 = ☐	

Double 7	
12 x 2	
Double 14	
8 x 2	
2 x 9	
Double 6	
Double 11	

Use this space for your notes and working out.

You can use your number bonds to 10 to help you with other problems

1	2	3	4	5	6	7	8	9	10
11	12	13	14	15	16	17	18	19	20

If you know, $7 + 3 = 10$

You can use this grid to show that, $17 + 3 = 20$

If you know, $10 - 2 = 8$

You can use this grid to show that, $20 - 12 = 8$

Addition to 20

Read out the whole sum and give the answer.

So for example,

$5 + \boxed{} = 20$ would be:

"Five add fifteen equals twenty"

$5 + \boxed{15} = 20$

Remember your number bonds to 10. They'll help!

$5 + \boxed{} = 20$						
$14 + \boxed{} = 20$						
$7 + \boxed{} = 20$						
$10 + \boxed{} = 20$						
$2 + \boxed{} = 20$						
$\boxed{} + 9 = 20$						
$16 + \boxed{} = 20$						
$0 + \boxed{} = 20$						
$\boxed{} + 3 = 20$						
$12 + \boxed{} = 20$						
$\boxed{} + 1 = 20$						
$11 + \boxed{} = 20$						
$\boxed{} + 4 = 20$						

Use this space for your notes and working out.

Subtraction from 20

Use this space for your notes and working out.

Read out the whole sum.

So for example,

$$20 - \square = 6$$

You say "Twenty take away fourteen equals six"

$$20 - \boxed{14} = 6$$

You must earn three consecutive ticks.

$20 - \square = 6$						
$20 - \square = 9$						
$20 - 4 = \square$						
$20 - \square = 17$						
$20 - 16 = \square$						
$20 - \square = 10$						
$20 - 12 = \square$						
$20 - \square = 1$						
$20 - \square = 5$						
$20 - 8 = \square$						
$20 - 3 = \square$						
$20 - \square = 18$						
$20 - \square = 6$						

More halving

Say the number that is half of these numbers.

For example,
18   You should say,
      "Half of eighteen is nine"

      $18 \div 2 = 9$

Don't forget that halving numbers is the same as dividing by 2.

Look

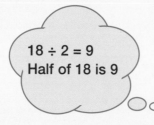

$18 \div 2 = 9$
Half of 18 is 9

18							
24							
22							
30							
14							
26							
12							
16							
28							
32							
20							
34							
10							

Use this space for your notes and working out.

Adding on 10s

This 100 square is really useful to add on 10's.

Each time you move one square down - you add on 10.

So,   14 + 30 would be

14
24
34
44

+10 ↓
+20 ↓
+30 ↓

14 + 30 = $\boxed{44}$

1	2	3	4	5	6	7	8	9	10
11	12	13	14	15	16	17	18	19	20
21	22	23	24	25	26	27	28	29	30
31	32	33	34	35	36	37	38	39	40
41	42	43	44	45	46	47	48	49	50
51	52	53	54	55	56	57	58	59	60
61	62	63	64	65	66	67	68	69	70
71	72	73	74	75	76	77	78	79	80
81	82	83	84	85	86	87	88	89	90
91	92	93	94	95	96	97	98	99	100

Adding on 10s

Read out the whole sum and the answer.

So for example,

17 + 30 would be:

17...27...37...47

(add on three lots of ten)

17 + 30 = $\boxed{47}$

17 + 30 = ☐							
42 + 50 = ☐							
69 + 20 = ☐							
33 + 30 = ☐							
11 + 20 = ☐							
47 + 60 = ☐							
37 + 10 = ☐							
45 + 40 = ☐							
16 + 50 = ☐							
13 + 70 = ☐							
80 + 21 = ☐							
10 + 67 = ☐							
15 + 80 = ☐							

Use this space for your notes and working out.

Adding 19

Use this space for your notes and working out.

A quick way to add 19 is to add 20 and then take away 1.

So for example,

$38 + 19$ would be:

$38 + 20 = 58$
$58 - 1 = 57$

So, $38 + 19 = \boxed{57}$

Read out the whole sum and give the answer.

38 + 19 = ☐							
26 + 19 = ☐							
47 + 19 = ☐							
13 + 19 = ☐							
19 + 19 = ☐							
19 + 42 = ☐							
58 + 19 = ☐							
49 + 19 = ☐							
19 + 65 = ☐							
104 + 19 = ☐							
19 + 15 = ☐							
120 + 19 = ☐							
12 + 19 = ☐							

Pairs of multiples of 10

You can use the facts you know about number bonds to 10 to help you with larger numbers.

If you know that
$$7 + 3 = 10$$

Then you also know that
$$70 + 30 = 100$$

Why is this?

Read the whole question You must get three consecutive ticks.

70 + 30 = ☐						
10 + ☐ = 100						
100 – 40 = ☐						
50 + ☐ = 100						
100 – ☐ = 0						
100 – ☐ = 40						
☐ + 80 = 100						
60 + 40 = ☐						
90 + ☐ = 100						
30 + ☐ = 100						
☐ + 20 = 100						
100 – 70 = ☐						
50 + 50 = ☐						

Use this space for your notes and working out.

Addition and subtraction

Use this space for your notes and working out.

Addition and subtraction without crossing the 10s boundary.

It will help if you can split the numbers into tens and ones.

So for example,
48 – 13 would be:

$$40 + 8 = 48$$
$$10 + 3 = 13$$

$$40 - 10 = 30 \qquad 8 - 3 = 5$$

So, $48 - 13 = \boxed{35}$

48 – 13 = ☐	
23 + 14 = ☐	
35 + 24 = ☐	
78 – 71 = ☐	
12 + 37 = ☐	
36 – 5 = ☐	
49 – 31 = ☐	
67 + 22 = ☐	
23 + 45 = ☐	
64 – 31 = ☐	
15 + 24 = ☐	
31 + 38 = ☐	
11 + 34 = ☐	

Pick 'n' mix to 20

Read out the whole sum.

So for example

$$\Box + 13 = 20$$

You say,
"Seven add thirteen
equals twenty"

$$\boxed{7} + 13 = 20$$

You must earn three
consecutive ticks.

$\Box + 13 = 20$						
$8 + \Box = 20$						
$\Box + 1 = 20$						
$20 - \Box = 6$						
$20 - 15 = \Box$						
$\Box + 4 = 20$						
$18 + \Box = 20$						
$\Box + 7 = 20$						
$12 + \Box = 20$						
$20 - \Box = 4$						
$20 - \Box = 0$						
$3 + \Box = 20$						
$20 - \Box = 9$						

Use this space for your
notes and working out.

Adding 9 and 19

Use this space for your notes and working out.

Remember that a quick way to add 9 or 19, is to add 10 or 20 and then take away 1.

So for example,

$43 + 19$ would be:

$43 + 20 = 63$
$63 - 1 = 62$

So, $43 + 19 = \boxed{62}$

Read out the whole sum.

$43 + 19 = \square$							
$34 + 19 = \square$							
$83 + 9 = \square$							
$19 + 19 = \square$							
$19 + 29 = \square$							
$9 + 81 = \square$							
$58 + 19 = \square$							
$75 + 9 = \square$							
$9 + 66 = \square$							
$79 + 19 = \square$							
$9 + 22 = \square$							
$110 + 19 = \square$							
$17 + 9 = \square$							

Doubles

Say the number that is double these numbers.

13						
7						
15						
9						
16						
14						
8						

Pick 'n' mix to 10

Read out the whole sum.

You must get three consecutive ticks.

$10 - \square = 3$						
$10 - 4 = \square$						
$\square + 8 = 10$						
$0 + \square = 10$						
$\square + 7 = 10$						
$\square + 2 = 10$						
$1 + \square = 10$						

Use this space for your notes and working out.

Doubles

Adding 9 and 19

Use this space for your notes and working out.

What is double the number?

You must say,
"Double 10 is 20."

Can you remember a quick way to add 9 and 19?

Read out the whole sum.

Doubles						
11						
17						
19						
8						
18						
14						
12						

Adding						
19 + 47 = ☐						
19 + 61 = ☐						
28 + 9 = ☐						
35 + 19 = ☐						
9 + 16 = ☐						
79 + 19 = ☐						
19 + 21 = ☐						

Pick 'n' mix to 20

Read out the whole sum.

Halving

Say the number which is half of these numbers.

Use this space for your notes and working out.

20 − ☐ = 16							
20 − 5 = ☐							
☐ + 9 = 20							
8 + ☐ = 20							
20 − 13 = ☐							
6 + ☐ = 20							
12 + ☐ = 20							

14							
22							
18							
26							
32							
30							
16							

Recap grid

Use this space for your notes and working out.

Use this grid to fill in any work you have found difficult so far.

Write in your own questions or copy out the questions you found hard.

Don't forget that you still need three consecutive ticks.

Addition and subtraction

Addition and subtraction to make a multiple of 10.

Multiples of 10 are numbers which are divisible by 10.
10, 20, 30, 40, 50, 60, ...

You need to say what you need to add or subtract to make the multiple of 10.

For example, 56 ☐ = 60

You say,
"56 add 4 equals 60"

56 ☐ = 60								
43 ☐ = 50								
65 ☐ = 70								
22 ☐ = 20								
87 ☐ = 80								
143 ☐ = 150								
76 ☐ = 80								
189 ☐ = 190								
255 ☐ = 260								
61 ☐ = 70								
167 ☐ = 160								
34 ☐ = 40								
95 ☐ = 100								

Use this space for your notes and working out.

Addition and subtraction

Use this space for your notes and working out.

Single-digit numbers to two-digit numbers.

As always, read out the whole question.

67 + 5 = ☐	
42 – 7 = ☐	
54 + 8 = ☐	
3 + 49 = ☐	
23 – 6 = ☐	
87 – 8 = ☐	
46 – 8 = ☐	
35 + 6 = ☐	
4 + 27 = ☐	
53 – 6 = ☐	
61 + 9 = ☐	
53 – 8 = ☐	
5 + 37 = ☐	

Adding 100

Add 100 to these numbers.

Say the number which is 100 more than...

For example,　34

　　　You say　"134"

　　　34 + 100 = 134

You must earn three consecutive ticks.

34							
230							
126							
7							
890							
2,300							
1,205							
6,384							
150							
1,031							
7,000							
1,356							
609							

Use this space for your notes and working out.

Changing

Use this space for your notes and working out.

How do you change these numbers?

For example, 42 to 62

You say   "you add 20"

$$42 + 20 = 62$$

Another example, 69 to 19

You say   "you subtract 50"

$$69 - 50 = \boxed{19}$$

42 to 62							
27 to 37							
41 to 71							
6 to 86							
31 to 71							
23 to 93							
19 to 69							
63 to 103							
57 to 107							
18 to 98							
45 to 125							
21 to 91							
12 to 52							

Rounding

Round these numbers to the nearest 10.

You must say which multiple of 10 these numbers are nearest.

32 to the nearest 10 is 30
57 to the nearest 10 is 60

With "5s" always round UP to the next multiple of 10.

45 to the nearest 10 is 50.

32	
57	
45	
87	
104	
69	
85	
192	
95	
76	
12	
233	
72	

Use this space for your notes and working out.

Recap grid

Use this space for your notes and working out.

Use this grid to fill in any work you have found difficult so far.

Write in your own questions or copy out the questions you found hard.

Don't forget that you still need three consecutive ticks.

Multiplying by 10

When you multiply by 10, numbers become 10 **times** bigger.

thousands	hundreds	tens	ones
			8
		8	0

$8 \times 10 = 80$

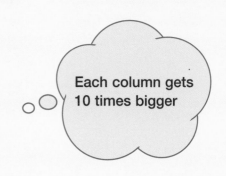

Each column gets 10 times bigger

Multiplying by 10

Use this space for your notes and working out.

Multiplying numbers by 10 is really important.

You must read out the whole sum.

For example, 2 x 10 = ☐

You say,   "Two times ten equals twenty"

2 x 10 = 20

2 x 10 = ☐	
5 x 10 = ☐	
7 x 10 = ☐	
3 x 10 = ☐	
10 x 6 = ☐	
4 x 10 = ☐	
10 x 10 = ☐	
10 x 12 = ☐	
15 x 10 = ☐	
0 x 10 = ☐	
10 x 11 = ☐	
10 x 1 = ☐	
8 x 10 = ☐	

Adding 90

Can you work out a quick way to add 90?

Yes, a quick way is to add 100 and then take away 10.

So for example,

50 + 90 would be:

50 + 100 = 150
150 – 10 = 140

So,   50 + 90 = 140

50 + 90 = ☐	
30 + 90 = ☐	
80 + 90 = ☐	
54 + 90 = ☐	
41 + 90 = ☐	
89 + 90 = ☐	
105 + 90 = ☐	
66 + 90 = ☐	
110 + 90 = ☐	
120 + 90 = ☐	
337 + 90 = ☐	
143 + 90 = ☐	
125 + 90 = ☐	

Use this space for your notes and working out.

Change from £1

Use this space for your notes and working out.

You need to say how much change you'll get from £1 if you spend these amounts.

To work this out, you can count on - up to 100.

For example, 27p

It is 3p to get up to 30
Then it's 70p to get to £1.

Altogether it is,

$$3p + 70p = 73p$$

27p							
65p							
78p							
12p							
37p							
89p							
45p							
50p							
6p							
71p							
63p							
24p							
85p							

Adding 29

Guess what you can do to add 29?

Yes the quick way is to add 30 and then take away 1.

So for example,

6 + 29 would be:

6 + 30 = 36
36 – 1 = 35

So, 6 + 29 = $\boxed{35}$

6 + 29 =							
25 + 29 =							
54 + 29 =							
24 + 29 =							
30 + 29 =							
29 + 49 =							
42 + 29 =							
60 + 29 =							
29 + 65 =							
112 + 29 =							
29 + 13 =							
120 + 29 =							
19 + 29 =							

Use this space for your notes and working out.

Doubling

Use this space for your notes and working out.

This is a really important skill.

You'll need to be really good at this to move on to the next stage.

Here's some more practice.

You say, "Double three is six"

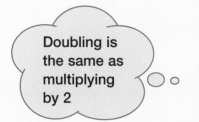

Doubling is the same as multiplying by 2

3	
7	
4	
8	
6	
9	
2	
10	
12	
14	
13	
0	
5	

Multiplying by 4

A quick way to multiply by 4 is to double and then double again.

So, if you want to know

     6 x 4

     Double 6 is 12
     Double 12 is 24.

So,   6 x 4 = 24

Good luck!

6							
5							
3							
4							
2							
1							
6							
10							
8							
9							
7							
0							
5							

Use this space for your notes and working out.

Odd and even

Use this space for your notes and working out.

Say whether these numbers are odd or even.

Even numbers are divisible by 2. Their ones digits are 0, 2, 4, 6 or 8

Odd numbers are not divisible by 2. Their ones digits are 1, 3, 5, 7 or 9

4						
13						
16						
10						
49						
81						
160						
269						
3040						
503						
8900						
67						
1						

Addition and subtraction

Addition and subtraction facts to 20.

Read out the whole fact.

For example,

$7 + 6 = \square$

You say, "Seven add six equals thirteen."

$7 + 6 = \boxed{13}$

$7 + 6 = \square$						
$5 + 9 = \square$						
$8 + 5 = \square$						
$6 + 3 = \square$						
$17 - 12 = \square$						
$9 - 4 = \square$						
$8 + 8 = \square$						
$4 + 7 = \square$						
$18 - 13 = \square$						
$3 + 9 = \square$						
$19 - 14 = \square$						
$20 - 7 = \square$						
$7 + 7 = \square$						

Use this space for your notes and working out.

More halving

Use this space for your notes and working out.

Halving numbers is really useful!

Remember that halving numbers is the same as dividing by 2.

For example, $18 \div 2 = \square$

You should say, "Eighteen divided by two is nine"

$$18 \div 2 = \boxed{9}$$

Read out the whole fact.

$18 \div 2 = \square$								
$24 \div 2 = \square$								
$22 \div 2 = \square$								
$30 \div 2 = \square$								
$14 \div 2 = \square$								
$26 \div 2 = \square$								
$36 \div 2 = \square$								
$16 \div 2 = \square$								
$28 \div 2 = \square$								
$32 \div 2 = \square$								
$20 \div 2 = \square$								
$34 \div 2 = \square$								
$10 \div 2 = \square$								

Adding on 11

A quick way to add 11 to any number is firstly to add ten (10) to it, and then to add the extra one (1).

So for example,

8 + 11 would be:

8 + 10 = 18
18 + 1 = 19

So,   8 + 11 = $\boxed{19}$

Read out the whole sum and give the answer.

8 + 11 = ☐							
24 + 11 = ☐							
58 + 11 = ☐							
39 + 11 = ☐							
11 + 20 = ☐							
47 + 11 = ☐							
11 + 125 = ☐							
357 + 11 = ☐							
11 + 450 = ☐							
11 + 92 = ☐							
183 + 11 = ☐							
18 + 11 = ☐							
11 + 90 = ☐							

Use this space for your notes and working out.

Facts to 20

Use this space for your notes and working out.

You can use the facts that you already know to answer these questions.

For example,

You know, $5 + 6 = 11$

So, you can work out,

$$50 + 60 = 110$$

Try out your method with these.

Read out the whole sum.

50 + 60 =☐									
30 + 50 =☐									
70 + 40 =☐									
20 + 90 =☐									
130 + 80 =☐									
120 + 70 =☐									
200 − 70 =☐									
70 + 80 =☐									
100 − 60 =☐									
150 − 70 =☐									
90 + 90 =☐									
180 − 110 =☐									
200 − 50 =☐									

Recap grid

Use this grid to put in any questions you have found difficult.

You can also make up your own questions.

Change from £1

Give the change you'd get from £1 after spending these amounts.

Use this space for your notes and working out.

51p						
76p						
6p						
14p						
43p						
89p						
22p						

Odds and evens

Rounding

Use this space for your notes and working out.

Say whether these numbers are odd or even.

Round these numbers to the nearest 10.

13	
450	
62	
55	
2,853	
100	
987	

43	
76	
135	
204	
98	
155	
81	

Halving

Halve these numbers.

You say, "Half of 12 is ..."

Multiplying by 4

Remember that you can double and then double again to multiply by 4.

Use this space for your notes and working out.

12	
26	
34	
16	
38	
32	
36	

6 x 4 = ☐	
3 x 4 = ☐	
8 x 4 = ☐	
12 x 4 = ☐	
5 x 4 = ☐	
7 x 4 = ☐	
4 x 4 = ☐	

Dividing by 4

Use this space for your notes and working out.

A quick way to divide by 4 is to halve and then halve again.

This is because ÷ 2 and then ÷ 2 again is the same as ÷ 4.

So, if you want to know

$$20 ÷ 4$$

$$20 ÷ 2 = 10$$
$$10 ÷ 2 = 5$$

So,   20 ÷ 4 = 5

20 ÷ 4 = ☐								
12 ÷ 4 = ☐								
32 ÷ 4 = ☐								
8 ÷ 4 = ☐								
24 ÷ 4 = ☐								
40 ÷ 4 = ☐								
4 ÷ 4 = ☐								
16 ÷ 4 = ☐								
28 ÷ 4 = ☐								
36 ÷ 4 = ☐								
60 ÷ 4 = ☐								
44 ÷ 4 = ☐								
80 ÷ 4 = ☐								

Fractions

Read out these fractions.

$\frac{1}{2}$ is "a half"

$\frac{1}{3}$ is "one third"

$\frac{1}{4}$ is "one quarter"

$\frac{3}{4}$ is "three quarters"

$\frac{2}{3}$ is "two thirds"

$\frac{1}{2}$						
$\frac{1}{3}$						
$\frac{3}{4}$						
$\frac{1}{4}$						
$\frac{2}{3}$						
$\frac{1}{3}$						
$\frac{3}{4}$						
$\frac{1}{2}$						
$\frac{1}{4}$						
$\frac{1}{3}$						
$\frac{3}{4}$						
$\frac{2}{3}$						
$\frac{1}{2}$						

Use this space for your notes and working out.

Naming digits

Use this space for your notes and working out.

You need to say the value of the **bold** digit in these numbers.

For example,

43   the 4 is 4 tens (40)

15**6**   the 6 is 6 ones (6)

2,**8**90   the 8 is 8 hundreds (800)

9,750, the 9 is 9 thousands (9000)

6,**0**45   the 0 is 0 hundreds

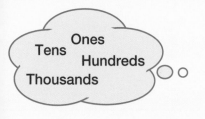
Ones
Tens
Hundreds
Thousands

43						
15**3**						
751						
1,9**5**6						
9,056						
3,**7**50						
5,9**8**0						
6,453						
495						
5,**1**00						
7,80**9**						
6,**0**08						
2,2**2**2						

Worded problems

These problems are revision of the things you've already done. They're written in a slightly different way.

Read out the question and then the answer.

For example,

"Take 7 from 12, you get 5"

Good luck!

Take 7 from 12						
Add 6 to 15						
16 divided by 2						
2 lots of 6						
34 subtract 24						
18 add 19						
Take 11 from 31						
24 divided by 4						
29 add 64						
9 multiplied by 4						
Double 16						
7 add 3						
15 take away 6						

Use this space for your notes and working out.

Using doubles

Use this space for your notes and working out.

Your doubling skills can help you work out other problems.

For example, if you know that double 17 is 34 then 17 + 17 = 34

So, 17 + 18 must be one more than this!

And, 17 + 19 must be two more than this!

Explain how you do them.

Double 17						
17 + 18 = ☐						
16 + 18 = ☐						
Double 13						
13 + 14 = ☐						
12 + 13 = ☐						
Double 25						
25 + 26 = ☐						
25 + 27 = ☐						
Double 19						
19 + 18 = ☐						
19 + 17 = ☐						
18 + 20 = ☐						

Recap grid

Use this grid to fill in any work you have found difficult so far.

Copy out the questions you found hard or write in your own questions.

Don't forget that you still need three consecutive ticks.

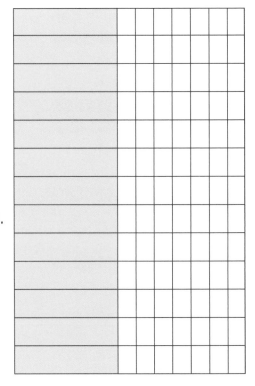

Use this space for your notes and working out.

Page 84 started on: _ _ _ _ _ _ _ _ _ _ _

Page 84 finished on: _ _ _ _ _ _ _ _ _ _ _ _

x and ÷ facts

Use this space for your notes and working out.

x and ÷ facts of 2 and 10.

If you know facts about multiplying, then you can work out division facts.

You need to say the division or multiplication fact which go with these.

For example, 2 x 7 = 14

You need to say, "14 divided by 2 equals 7"

14 ÷ 2 = 7

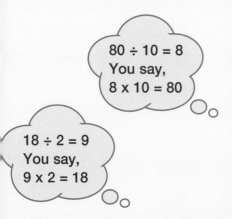

80 ÷ 10 = 8
You say,
8 x 10 = 80

18 ÷ 2 = 9
You say,
9 x 2 = 18

2 x 7 = 14							
10 x 5 = 50							
8 x 2 = 16							
18 ÷ 2 = 9							
7 x 10 = 70							
12 ÷ 2 = 6							
80 ÷ 8 = 10							
4 x 2 = 8							
4 x 10 = 40							
10 x 2 = 20							
16 ÷ 2 = 8							
9 x 10 = 90							
2 x 3 = 6							

Adding 1, 11, 21, 31, 41...

This page is all about adding and subtracting numbers which have 1 in the ones column.

A way you can do these is round the numbers to the nearest 10, and then add or subtract the extra 1.

For example, 38 + 21 = ☐ would be, 38 + 20 = 58 then add the extra one,

so,   38 + 21 = 59

38 + 21 = ☐						
66 + 31 = ☐						
84 − 31 = ☐						
97 + 41 = ☐						
51 + 21 = ☐						
61 + 138 = ☐						
135 − 51 = ☐						
11 + 94 = ☐						
59 + 31 = ☐						
136 + 41 = ☐						
74 − 21 = ☐						
41 + 125 = ☐						
87 + 31 = ☐						

Use this space for your notes and working out.

Negative numbers

Use this space for your notes and working out.

You need to say which number is the smallest.

Some examples for you,

6 and 12   You say,
"6 is the smaller number"

5 and −7   You say,
"Minus seven is the smaller number"

You must earn three consecutive ticks.

```
5
4
3
2
1
0
−1
−2
−3
−4
−5
```

6 and 12							
5 and −7							
−4 and 0							
−2 and 12							
3 and −9							
−18 and −14							
14 and 8							
10 and −11							
−8 and −6							
−12 and 0							
3 and −1							
0 and −1							
5 and −4							

**More great division
÷2 and ÷4**

Remember your ways to
divide by 2 and 4.

Don't forget to read out
the whole question.

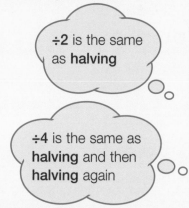

÷2 is the same
as **halving**

÷4 is the same as
halving and then
halving again

16 ÷ 2 = ☐							
16 ÷ 4 = ☐							
28 ÷ 4 = ☐							
62 ÷ 2 = ☐							
24 ÷ 4 = ☐							
20 ÷ 4 = ☐							
56 ÷ 2 = ☐							
18 ÷ 2 = ☐							
64 ÷ 4 = ☐							
36 ÷ 2 = ☐							
48 ÷ 2 = ☐							
100 ÷ 4 = ☐							
52 ÷ 2 = ☐							

Use this space for your
notes and working out.

Adding 39

Use this space for your notes and working out.

Solve these addition problems.

They're all about adding 39.

A quick method to add 39 is to add 40 and then subtract one.

For example, 15 + 39 = ☐

$$15 + 40 = 55$$
$$55 - 1 = 54$$

So,   15 + 39 = $\boxed{54}$

Read out the whole sum.

15 + 39 = ☐							
28 + 39 = ☐							
52 + 39 = ☐							
39 + 43 = ☐							
65 + 39 = ☐							
39 + 39 = ☐							
39 + 54 = ☐							
96 + 39 = ☐							
39 + 43 = ☐							
149 + 39 = ☐							
164 + 39 = ☐							
39 + 20 = ☐							
13 + 39 = ☐							

Multiplying by 100

When you multiply by 100, numbers become 100 times bigger.

For example, 12 x 100

You say,   "Twelve times one hundred equals one thousand two hundred"

$$12 \times 100 = 1200$$

Read out the whole sum.

12 x 100 = ☐	
65 x 100 = ☐	
43 x 100 = ☐	
7 x 100 = ☐	
100 x 50 = ☐	
3 x 100 = ☐	
10 x 100 = ☐	
100 x 97 = ☐	
83 x 100 = ☐	
0 x 100 = ☐	
100 x 11 = ☐	
100 x 1 = ☐	
19 x 100 = ☐	

Use this space for your notes and working out.

More change from £1

Use this space for your notes and working out.

This is a really important skill. You need to say how much change you'll get from £1 if you spend these amounts.

To work this out, you can count on - up to 100.

For example, 18p

It is 2p to get up to 20p
Then it's 80p to get to £1.

Altogether it is,
     2p + 80p = 82p

18p							
52p							
73p							
7p							
35p							
78p							
34p							
69p							
4p							
61p							
26p							
3p							
38p							

Adding 1s, 10s and 100s

You need to be able to add ones, tens and hundreds to any number.

You must read out the whole sum.

You need to earn three consecutive ticks.

18 + 10 = ☐	
75 + 300 = ☐	
143 + 1 = ☐	
503 + 80 = ☐	
200 + 680 = ☐	
54 + 90 = ☐	
74 + 5 = ☐	
51 + 300 = ☐	
40 + 380 = ☐	
254 + 80 = ☐	
900 + 360 = ☐	
368 + 7 = ☐	
800 + 200 = ☐	

Use this space for your notes and working out.

Sequences

Use this space for your notes and working out.

A sequence is a group of numbers which have a rule.

So, for example, the sequence 2, 4, 6, 8, 10 has a rule add 2 each time.

You'll need to read the whole sequence and then work out the next two numbers.

For example,
12, 14, 16 , 18, ☐ , ☐

You say,
"12, 14, 16 , 18, 20 , 22 "

12, 14, 16, 18					
1, 3, 5, 7,					
24, 26, 28,					
13, 15, 17, 19,					
3, 6, 9, 12,					
21, 23, 25,					
35, 37, 39,					
4, 8, 12, 16,					
20, 25, 30,					
10, 13, 16, 19					
24, 28, 32,					
85, 90, 95,					
65, 67, 69,					

Recap grid

Use this grid to fill in any work you have found difficult so far.

You can also put in your own questions.

Dividing by 4

Can you remember a way to divide by 4?

A quick way is to halve and halve again.

$8 \div 4 =$ ☐					
$32 \div 4 =$ ☐					
$36 \div 4 =$ ☐					
$24 \div 4 =$ ☐					
$80 \div 4 =$ ☐					
$64 \div 4 =$ ☐					
$20 \div 4 =$ ☐					

Use this space for your notes and working out.

Fractions

Naming digits

Use this space for your notes and working out.

Read out these fractions.

You need to say the value of the **bold** digit in these numbers.

$\frac{3}{4}$	
$\frac{2}{3}$	
$\frac{1}{4}$	
$\frac{1}{3}$	
$\frac{3}{4}$	
$\frac{1}{3}$	
$\frac{1}{2}$	

651	
9,0**0**8	
68**9**	
508	
2,098	
8,6**3**2	
40**7**	

Worded problems

You need to read out the whole sentence and then the answer.

Using doubles

Use the doubles facts that you know to work out the answers to these.

Read out the whole question.

Use this space for your notes and working out.

16 divided by 2							
2 lots of 6							
34 subtract 24							
18 add 19							
Take 11 from 31							
24 divided by 4							
6 multiplied by 4							

Double 17							
17 + 18 = ☐							
16 + 18 = ☐							
Double 26							
25 + 26 = ☐							
25 + 27 = ☐							
26 + 28 = ☐							

Nines

Use this space for your notes and working out.

This section is to give you practice at adding numbers with a 9 in the ones column.

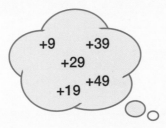

+9   +39
   +29
+19   +49

Remember the quick way of adding on the number to the nearest 10, and then taking away 1.

4 + 19 = ☐								
39 + 53 = ☐								
17 + 29 = ☐								
75 + 9 = ☐								
49 + 38 = ☐								
24 + 39 = ☐								
86 + 19 = ☐								
91 + 29 = ☐								
64 + 9 = ☐								
29 + 39 = ☐								
9 + 97 = ☐								
99 + 19 = ☐								
40 + 29 = ☐								

Multiplication

Multiplication facts up to 5 x 5.

It's really useful to know these multiplication facts.

You have already had a lot of practice with multiplication. Remember these

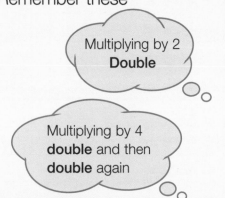

Multiplying by 2
Double

Multiplying by 4
double and then **double** again

2 x 2 =							
3 x 4 =							
2 x 5 =							
5 x 3 =							
4 x 4 =							
5 x 5 =							
3 x 0 =							
4 x 2 =							
5 x 4 =							
3 x 2 =							
1 x 5 =							
3 x 3 =							
2 x 1 =							

Use this space for your notes and working out.

Less than <   greater than >

Use this space for your notes and working out.

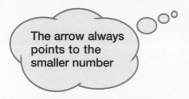
The arrow always points to the smaller number

There is more than one correct answer, you need to put any correct number into the sentence.

< 3   You could say,
      "2 is less than 3"

7 >   You could say,
      "7 is greater than 5"

Read the whole sentence.

Less than <

Greater than >

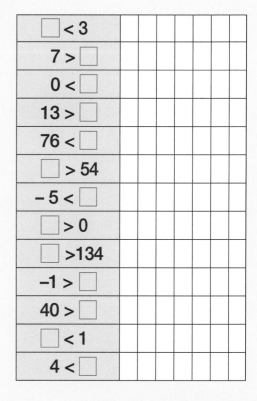

☐ < 3							
7 > ☐							
0 < ☐							
13 > ☐							
76 < ☐							
☐ > 54							
– 5 < ☐							
☐ > 0							
☐ > 134							
–1 > ☐							
40 > ☐							
☐ < 1							
4 < ☐							

Congratulations!

You have successfully completed the first
100 pages of Power of 2

Well Done.

**You should be
proud of yourself.**

Addition and subtraction

Addition and subtraction to 20

Read the whole question.

4 + 14 = ☐	
19 – 7 = ☐	
☐ + 6 = 19	
17 – ☐ = 3	
☐ – 5 = 8	
☐ + 9 = 17	
20 –11 = ☐	

Dividing by 2 and 4

Read the whole question.

38 ÷ 2 = ☐	
84 ÷ 4 = ☐	
56 ÷ 2 = ☐	
64 ÷ 4 = ☐	
46 ÷ 2 = ☐	
56 ÷ 4 = ☐	
22 ÷ 2 = ☐	

Use this space for your notes and working out.

Multiplying by 10 and 100

Negative numbers

Use this space for your notes and working out.

Remember how you multiply numbers by 10 and 100.

You need to say which is the largest of these numbers.

5 x 100 = ☐						
10 x 76 = ☐						
43 x 100 = ☐						
390 x 10 = ☐						
100 x 60 = ☐						
608 x 10 = ☐						
100 x 10 = ☐						

5, 8, 2						
–6, –10, –3						
–5, 0, –3						
6, –20, –5						
9, –10, 23						
86, 90, –100						
4, –4, 0						

Fractions and decimals

You need to say both the decimal and fraction for each of these.

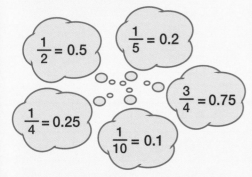

$\frac{1}{2} = 0.5$

$\frac{1}{5} = 0.2$

$\frac{3}{4} = 0.75$

$\frac{1}{4} = 0.25$

$\frac{1}{10} = 0.1$

For example,

$\frac{1}{2}$ You say, "One half equals nought point five"

$$\frac{1}{2} = 0.5$$

$\frac{1}{2}$							
$\frac{1}{5}$							
$\frac{1}{10}$							
$\frac{1}{4}$							
$\frac{3}{4}$							
$\frac{1}{5}$							
0.5							
0.25							
0.75							
0.1							
0.2							
$\frac{1}{10}$							
$\frac{1}{4}$							

Use this space for your notes and working out.

Recap grid

Use this space for your notes and working out.

Use this grid to fill in any work you have found difficult so far.

Copy out the questions you found hard or write in your own questions.

Don't forget that you still need three consecutive ticks.

Multiplication and division facts for 2, 3, 4, 5 and 10.

You need to read out the whole question.

Use the facts you already know to solve these.

For example,

$16 \div 4 = \square$

You say,
"16 divided by 4 equals 4"

$16 \div 4 = \boxed{4}$

$16 \div 4 = \square$							
$5 \times 3 = \square$							
$20 \div 5 = \square$							
$3 \times 3 = \square$							
$25 \div 5 = \square$							
$12 \div 3 = \square$							
$10 \div 2 = \square$							
$8 \times 10 = \square$							
$4 \times \square = 20$							
$\square \times 10 = 90$							
$3 \times \square = 15$							
$2 \times \square = 0$							
$5 \times 5 = \square$							

Use this space for your notes and working out.

Less than, greater than

Fractions and decimals

Use this space for your notes and working out.

Read out the statement.

Put in a number which makes the statement correct.

Say both the fraction and the decimal.

76 < ☐							
☐ > 54							
−5 < ☐							
☐ > 0							
☐ > 134							
−1 > ☐							
40 > ☐							

$\frac{1}{4}$							
$\frac{3}{4}$							
$\frac{1}{5}$							
0.5							
0.25							
0.75							
0.1							

The arrow always points to the smaller number

Page 107 started on: _ _ _ _ _ _ _ _ _ _ _ _ _

Page 107 finished on: _ _ _ _ _ _ _ _ _ _ _ _ _

Addition

Use the skills you know to work these problems out.

Read out the whole sum.

16 + 39 = ☐	
18 + ☐ = 37	
65 + 80 = ☐	
791 + 40 = ☐	
45 + 9 = ☐	
93 + 90 = ☐	
☐ + 49 = 67	

Multiplication and division

Facts for 2, 3, 4, 5 and 10.

Read out the whole fact.

5 x 4 = ☐	
60 ÷ ☐ = 10	
3 x 3 = ☐	
2 x ☐ = 10	
☐ x 4 = 12	
16 ÷ ☐ = 4	
5 x 5 = ☐	

Use this space for your notes and working out.

Adding numbers

Use this space for your notes and working out.

When you have to add up 3 or 4 small numbers, one way you can do it is to find pairs of numbers which total 10.

For example, $7 + 8 + 3 = \square$

because $7 + 3 = 10$

we can see that $10 + 8 = 18$

so, $7 + 8 + 3 = \boxed{18}$

8 + 5 + 2						
9 + 7 + 1						
3 + 6 + 4						
5 + 9 + 5						
4 + 8 + 6						
1 + 7 + 9 + 2						
2 + 6 + 8						
7 + 3 + 6						
9 + 6 + 4 + 2						
5 + 8 + 4 + 5						
3 + 8 + 7						
6 + 8 + 4						
2 + 8 + 7						

Time

Time is a very important area for using numbers.

You'll need to be able to work out how long it is between times and also know some facts about time.

You need to read these sentences and fill in the missing word or number.

1 week is ... days								
1 year is ... days								
1 day is ... hours								
1 hour is ... minutes								
There are ... minutes in half an hour								
1 leap year is ... days								
It is ... minutes from 2.00pm to 3.00pm								
There are ... minutes in a quarter of an hour								
It is ... minutes from 10.15am to 10.45am								
There are ... minutes in three-quarters of an hour								

Use this space for your notes and working out.

Doubles and halves

Use this space for your notes and working out.

Here's some more practice at doubling and halving.

Remember that...

> Doubling is the same as multiplying by 2

> Halving is the same as dividing by 2

Double 18							
Half of 48							
Double 65							
Half of 130							
75 x 2 = ☐							
36 x 2 = ☐							
47 x 2 = ☐							
Half of 72							
86 ÷ 2 = ☐							
Double 150							
130 ÷ 2 = ☐							
98 ÷ 2 = ☐							
55 x 2 = ☐							

Reading larger numbers

Reading large number isn't always easy.
This section will give you practice. You need
to know that each column gets 10 times bigger!

Use this space for your notes and working out.

hundred thousands	ten thousands	thousands,	hundreds	tens	ones
1	2	7 ,	7	8	9

One hundred and twenty seven thousand, seven hundred and eighty nine

12,680							
76,907							
127,789							
30,762							
76,086							
590,763							
405,629							

80,871							
20,067							
900,000							
708,076							
5,001							
11,813							
49,500							

Nearly numbers

Use this space for your notes and working out.

This section is about adding numbers with either a 1 or a 9 in the ones column.

Remember, a way to add 9, 19, 29 is to round it up to the nearest 10 and then subtract 1.

And a way to add 11, 21, 31, 41 is to round it down to the nearest 10 and then add 1.

43 + 19 =								
31 + 56 =								
74 + 29 =								
67 + 19 =								
41 + 34 =								
29 + 52 =								
69 + 25 =								
93 + 11 =								
29 + 29 =								
71 + 35 =								
64 + 99 =								
31 + 80 =								
19 + 19 =								

Making 1000

These are all numbers facts involving 1000. You must read out the whole fact.

For example,

$$700 + \square = 1000$$

So you say,

"Seven hundred add three hundred equals one thousand."

$$700 + 300 = 1000$$

Earn three consecutive ticks.

700 + □ = 1000							
900 + □ = 1000							
200 + □ = 1000							
□ + 400 = 1000							
500 + □ = 1000							
□ + 800 = 1000							
200+300+ □ =1000							
600+100+ □ =1000							
300+ □ +300 =1000							
□ + 300 = 1000							
500+200+ □ =1000							
100+300+ □ =1000							
600 + □ = 1000							

Use this space for your notes and working out.

Multiplying by 2, 3, 4 and 5

Multiplying by 10

Use this space for your notes and working out.

Read out the whole question.

Read out the whole question.

Earn three consecutive ticks.

4 x 4 = ☐	
3 x 5 = ☐	
10 x 4 = ☐	
5 x 2 = ☐	
3 x 4 = ☐	
0 x 3 = ☐	
3 x 3 = ☐	

8 x 10 = ☐	
10 x 10 = ☐	
10 x 5 = ☐	
14 x 10 = ☐	
26 x 10 = ☐	
10 x 0 = ☐	
9 x 10 = ☐	

Multiplying

Look at this example of multiplying by a multiple of 10.

$$50 \times 4 = \square$$

First you can multiply

$$5 \times 4 = 20$$

then you can multiply this by 10.

$$20 \times 10 = 200$$

So, $50 \times 4 = \boxed{200}$

50 x 4 = ☐							
30 x 3 = ☐							
40 x 5 = ☐							
60 x 2 = ☐							
10 x 8 = ☐							
40 x 3 = ☐							
20 x 4 = ☐							
5 x 30 = ☐							
40 x 2 = ☐							
50 x 5 = ☐							
20 x 5 = ☐							
14 x 10 = ☐							
20 x 2 = ☐							

Use this space for your notes and working out.

Doubles and halves

Use this space for your notes and working out.

More practice at doubling and halving.

Read out the whole question.

For example, Double 19

You say, "Double 19 is 38"

Halving is the same as dividing by 2

Double 19							
Half of 120							
Double 75							
46 x 2 = ☐							
Half of 74							
36 ÷ 2 = ☐							
49 x 2 = ☐							
Half of 240							
86 ÷ 2 = ☐							
Double 150							
130 ÷ 2 = ☐							
98 ÷ 2 = ☐							
35 x 2 = ☐							

Recap grid

Use this grid to fill in any work you have found difficult so far.

Copy out the questions you found hard or write in your own questions.

Don't forget that you still need three consecutive ticks.

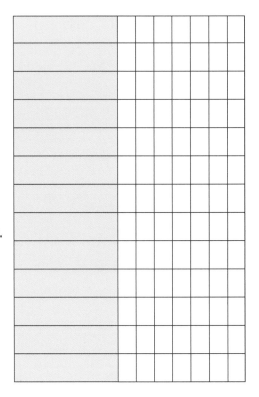

Use this space for your notes and working out.

Making multiples of 100

Use this space for your notes and working out.

What do you need to add or subtract to make a multiple of 100?

For example,

$$274 + \square = 300$$

One way to do this is to start with

$$274 \xrightarrow{+6} 280 \xrightarrow{+20} 300$$

So, $274 + \boxed{26} = 300$

$274 + \square = 300$							
$726 - \square = 700$							
$843 + \square = 900$							
$133 + \square = 200$							
$47 + \square = 100$							
$611 + \square = 700$							
$963 + \square = 1000$							
$185 - \square = 100$							
$\square + 555 = 600$							
$975 - \square = 900$							
$738 + \square = 800$							
$\square + 541 = 600$							
$175 + \square = 200$							

Sum to 15

This is a game for 2 players. Play the game and keep track of who wins.

The aim is to be the first person to get numbers which total 15.

Each player takes it in turns to pick a number from 1 2 3 4 5 6 7 8 9

Each number may only be picked once. The winner is the first person to get two, three or four numbers which add up to 15.

Here is an example game:

1 2 3 4 5 6 7 8 9

Player A goes first and chooses 6

Player A	Player B
6	

Player B can then choose
1 2 3 4 5 6 7 8 9

Player A	Player B
6	9

Player B chooses 9

Player A can then choose
1 2 3 4 5 6 7 8 9

Player A	Player B
6	9
5	

Player A chooses 5

Player B can then choose
1 2 3 4 5 6 7 8 9

Player A	Player B
6	9
5	3

Player B chooses 3

Player A can then choose

1 2 ~~3~~ 4 5 ~~6~~ 7 8 ~~9~~

Player A	Player B
6	9
5	3
4	

Player A chooses 4

Player A is the winner because

6 + 5 + 4 = 15

Overleaf are some grids for you to use.

Cross off the numbers when you have used them. Write your name at the top of the grid.

Example

1 2 ~~3 4 5 6 7 8~~ 9

Shermeena	Calvin
7	8
5	3
6	4

Calvin wins because

8 + 3 + 4 = 15

1 2 3 4 5 6 7 8 9

_ _ _ _ _ _ _ _ _ _ _ wins because
= 15

1 2 3 4 5 6 7 8 9

_ _ _ _ _ _ _ _ _ _ _wins because
= 15

Use this space for your notes and working out.

1 2 3 4 5 6 7 8 9

_ _ _ _ _ _ _ _ _ _ _wins because
= 15

1 2 3 4 5 6 7 8 9

_ _ _ _ _ _ _ _ _ _ _wins because
= 15

Use this space for your notes and working out.

1 2 3 4 5 6 7 8 9

_ _ _ _ _ _ _ _ _ _ _wins because

= 15

1 2 3 4 5 6 7 8 9

_ _ _ _ _ _ _ _ _ _wins because

= 15

1 2 3 4 5 6 7 8 9

_ _ _ _ _ _ _ _ _ _ _wins because

= 15

1 2 3 4 5 6 7 8 9

_ _ _ _ _ _ _ _ _ _wins because

= 15

Subtracting four-digit numbers

These are all subtracting a four-digit number from another four-digit number.

For example,

$3462 - 3452 = \square$

You can count on from 52 to 62.

So, $3462 - 3452 = \boxed{10}$

3462 – 3452 =							
4064 – 4055 =							
5834 – 5822 =							
9675 – 9666 =							
1329 – 1320 =							
6192 – 6185 =							
7348 – 7334 =							
3004 – 2998 =							
5731 – 5726 =							
9743 – 9731 =							
8751 – 8738 =							
5607 – 5599 =							
7054 – 7043 =							

Use this space for your notes and working out.

Use this space for your notes and working out.

It's really useful to know the multiplication facts.

You've already had some practice, these contain even more facts.

Read out the whole fact.

For example, 3 x 8 = ☐

You say,

"3 times 8 equals 24"

3 x 8 = 24

Multiplying by 4
double and then
double again

3 x 8 = ☐	
5 x 6 = ☐	
2 x 7 = ☐	
10 x 2 = ☐	
4 x 6 = ☐	
☐ x 5 = 40	
4 x 8 = ☐	
9 x 3 = ☐	
5 x 9 = ☐	
3 x ☐ = 27	
4 x 7 = ☐	
9 x 4 = ☐	
4 x 4 = ☐	

Addition and subtraction

Addition and subtraction of 2-digit numbers

These numbers all have 2 digits. You need to read out the whole fact.
You must earn three consecutive ticks.

A strategy you can use,

$$93 - 47 = \boxed{}$$

You can count on from 47 to 93.

$$47 \underset{+3}{\nearrow} 50 \underset{+40}{\nearrow} 90 \underset{+3}{\nearrow} 93$$

So, $93 - 47 = \boxed{46}$

93 − 47 = ☐							
23 + 56 = ☐							
86 + 35 = ☐							
75 − 46 = ☐							
98 − 13 = ☐							
24 + 37 = ☐							
58 + 15 = ☐							
91 − 19 = ☐							
36 + 76 = ☐							
55 + 26 = ☐							
87 − 66 = ☐							
77 − 28 = ☐							
75 − 25 = ☐							

Use this space for your notes and working out.

Time

Use this space for your notes and working out.

Time is a very important area for using numbers.

You'll need to be able to work out how long it is between times and also know some facts about time.

You need to read these sentences and fill in the missing word or number.

1 year is ... months							
12 o'clock add one hour is ...							
8.30am to 8.45am is ... minutes							
5.15am to 5.45am is ... minutes							
3.30pm to 4.10pm is ... minutes							
8.45pm to 10.00pm is ... minutes							
1 day is ... hours							
50 minutes before 8.00pm is ...							
6.40pm to 7.00pm is ... minutes							
50 minutes before 1.00pm is ...							
2.25am to 3.00am is ... minutes							
45 minutes before 1.00pm is ...							

Using doubles

You can use the doubles facts that you know to add 2 numbers which are close to each other.

Here are some tips:

16 + 18 is double 18 and then subtract 2.

70 + 80 is double 70 and then add 10

47 + 45 is double 45 and then add 2.

17 + 17 = ☐								
17 + 18 = ☐								
Double 35								
38 + 35 = ☐								
Double 15								
14 + 16 = ☐								
32 x 2 = ☐								
29 + 32 = ☐								
Double 150								
160 + 170								
Double 300								
280 + 290 = ☐								
295 + 295 = ☐								

Use this space for your notes and working out.

It's good to show how you worked it out

Counting on

Use this space for your notes and working out.

This section will help you to know and learn your times-tables.

You need to read out the three numbers and then continue the sequence. You must say the next three numbers.

For example,
4, 8, 12, ..., ..., ...

You say,
"4, 8, 12, 16, 20, 24"

4, 8, 12, ...						
3, 6, 9, ...						
10, 15, 20, ...						
40, 50, 60, ...						
6, 12, 18, ...						
2, 4, 6, ...						
9, 18, 27, ...						
9, 12, 15, ...						
12, 16, 20, ...						
7, 14, 21, ...						
35, 40, 45, ...						
8, 16, 24, ...						
60, 70, 80, ...						

Reading large numbers

Read out these numbers.

Earn three consecutive ticks.

Nearly numbers

Use what you have learnt to add and subtract 11, 21, 31, 41 and 9, 19, 29, 39, 49

Use this space for your notes and working out.

680,451							
908,620							
50,577							
60,060							
400,000							
300,350							
629,701							

29 + 25 = ☐							
56 + 11 = ☐							
39 + 29 = ☐							
41 + 37 = ☐							
34 + 99 = ☐							
81 + 120 = ☐							
31 + 69 = ☐							

Time

Making 1000

Use this space for your notes and working out.

Read out the whole sentence.

Read out the whole sentence.

20 minutes before 8.00 is ...								
5.40am to 6.00am is ... mins								
40 minutes before 1.00 is ...								
7.25am to 8.00am is ... mins								
45 mins before 6.00pm is ...								
8.35 to 9.05 is ... minutes								
25 minutes after 6.30pm is ...								

200 + ☐ = 1000								
700 + ☐ = 1000								
400 + ☐ = 1000								
☐ + 500 = 1000								
300 + ☐ = 1000								
☐ + 800 = 1000								
900 + ☐ = 1000								

Multiplying by multiples of 10

Read out the whole sentence.

40 x 4 = ☐						
20 x 5 = ☐						
5 x 30 = ☐						
40 x ☐ = 80						
5 x 50 = ☐						
30 x 3 = ☐						
17 x 10 = ☐						

Addition and subtraction

Addition and subtraction to multiples of 100.

Read out the whole question.

Use this space for your notes and working out.

234 + ☐ = 300						
26 + ☐ = 100						
465 + ☐ = 500						
863 + ☐ = 900						
121 + ☐ = 200						
☐ + 515 = 600						
975 − ☐ = 900						

Doubles and halves

Subtracting 4-digit numbers

Use this space for your notes and working out.

Read out the whole statement.

Earn three consecutive ticks.

You just need to give the answer to these questions.

Double 85						
36 x 2 =						
Half of 54						
36 ÷ 2 =						
59 x 2 =						
Half of 140						
76 ÷ 2 =						

3433 – 3425 =						
8674 – 8667 =						
1459 – 1440 =						
6212 – 6201 =						
7349 – 7336 =						
5004 – 4997 =						
1131 – 1125 =						

Multiplying

Multiplying by 2, 3, 4, 5 and 10

Read out the whole question.

Counting on

Read these sequences and say the next three numbers.

Use this space for your notes and working out.

$4 \times 7 = \square$	
$\square \times 5 = 35$	
$8 \times 3 = \square$	
$2 \times 7 = \square$	
$4 \times 9 = \square$	
$3 \times \square = 21$	
$3 \times 6 = \square$	

6, 12, 18, ...	
2, 4, 6, ...	
9, 18, 27, ...	
8, 16, 24, ...	
16, 20, 24, ...	
7, 14, 21, ...	
70, 80, 90, ...	

Using near doubles

Use this space for your notes and working out.

Use the doubles facts that you know to answer these.

Earn three consecutive ticks.

Double 45							
$48 + 45 = \square$							
Double 17							
$17 + 18 = \square$							
$37 \times 2 = \square$							
$38 + 37 = \square$							
Double 370							

Less than, greater than

Read out the statement.

Put in a number which makes the statement correct.

$26 < \square$							
$\square > 4$							
$-7 < \square$							
$\square > 0$							
$\square > 204$							
$-10 > \square$							
$50 > \square$							

Recap grid

Use this grid to fill in any work you have found difficult so far.

Copy out the questions you found hard or write in your own questions.

Don't forget that you still need three consecutive ticks.

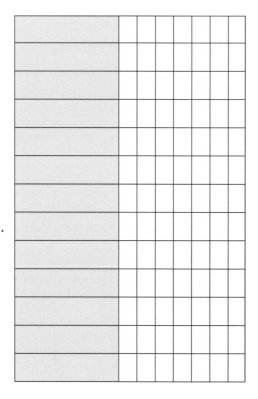

Use this space for your notes and working out.

Multiplication facts

Use this space for your notes and working out.

Multiplication facts for 2, 3, 4, 5 and 10

You need to read out the whole question.

Use the facts you already know to solve these.

For example, 8 x 4 = ☐

You say,
"8 multiplied by 4 equals 32"

8 x 4 = 32

8 x 4 = ☐							
5 x 9 = ☐							
6 x 5 = ☐							
3 x 3 = ☐							
4 x 7 = ☐							
9 x 3 = ☐							
8 x 5 = ☐							
8 x 3 = ☐							
4 x ☐ = 20							
☐ x 10 = 90							
3 x ☐ = 18							
4 x 6 = ☐							
5 x 5 = ☐							

Division facts

Division facts for 2, 3, 4, 5 and 10.

Division facts are related to the multiplication facts that you know.

Look at this

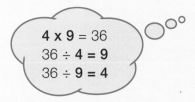

4 x 9 = 36
36 ÷ 4 = 9
36 ÷ 9 = 4

Read out the whole fact.

3 x 8 = ☐							
24 ÷ 3 = ☐							
4 x 6 = ☐							
24 ÷ 4 = ☐							
5 x 9 = ☐							
45 ÷ 9 = ☐							
45 ÷ 5 = ☐							
9 x 3 = ☐							
27 ÷ 3 = ☐							
4 x 7 = ☐							
28 ÷ ☐ = 7							
5 x 4 = ☐							
20 ÷ 4 = ☐							

Use this space for your notes and working out.

Dividing

Use this space for your notes and working out.

Dividing a multiple of 100 by 10.

When you divide by 10, the number becomes 10 times smaller.

The digits move one place to the right.

Look at this example,

$$600 \div 10 = \square$$

You say, $600 \div 10 = \boxed{60}$

60 is 10 times smaller than 600.

$600 \div 10 = \square$	
$300 \div 10 = \square$	
$100 \div 10 = \square$	
$900 \div 10 = \square$	
$1000 \div 10 = \square$	
$1400 \div 10 = \square$	
$700 \div 10 = \square$	
$\square \div 10 = 50$	
$1100 \div 10 = \square$	
$500 \div 10 = \square$	
$700 \div \square = 70$	
$\square \div 10 = 40$	
$200 \div 10 = \square$	

Time

Here's more practice at working out times.

You need to read the questions and earn three consecutive ticks.

Use this space for your notes and working out.

What time will it be 1 hour after 11 o'clock?							
It is 7.40pm. How many minutes is it until 8.00pm?							
How many minutes is it from 3.40am to 4.10am?							
What is the time 50 minutes before 9.00am?							
It is 4.45pm. How many minutes is it until 5.15pm?							
How many minutes is it from 12.20pm to 1.10pm?							
What is the time 40 minutes before 10.10am?							
It is 7.40pm. How many minutes is it until 8.00pm?							
What time will it be $1\frac{1}{2}$ hours after 3 o'clock?							

Multiplying by 10

Use this space for your notes and working out.

When you multiply numbers by 10 the digits move one place to the left.

Look at these examples:

68 x 10 = ☐
68 x 10 = 680

10 x ☐ = 430
10 x 43 = 430

> **Multiplying by 10** makes numbers **10 times bigger**

68 x 10 = ☐							
10 x 12 = ☐							
41 x 10 = ☐							
10 x 84 = ☐							
10 x 50 = ☐							
32 x 10 = ☐							
☐ x 10 = 860							
10 x 70 = ☐							
19 x 10 = ☐							
☐ x 10 = 420							
10 x 12 = ☐							
10 x ☐ = 300							
75 x 10 = ☐							

Doubling multiples of 10

You have already done doubles of numbers.

You can use these to find the doubles of multiples of 10.

Two examples,

Double 14 is 28

    So double 140 is 280

Double 27 is 54

    So double 270 is 540

Double 120						
Double 300						
420 x 2 = ☐						
70 x 2 = ☐						
2 x 130 = ☐						
Double 230						
Double 350						
320 x 2 = ☐						
290 x 2 = ☐						
Double 460						
2 x 170 = ☐						
190 x 2 = ☐						
Double 80						

Use this space for your notes and working out.

Read out the statement and give the answer

Halving multiples of 10

Use this space for your notes and working out.

Halving numbers is the opposite of doubling.

Look at this example:

Half of **520**

Half of 52 is 26

So half of 520 is 260

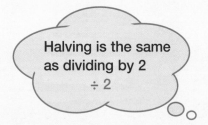

Halving is the same
as dividing by 2
÷ 2

Half of 520						
240 ÷ 2 = ☐						
160 ÷ 2 = ☐						
Half of 900						
360 ÷ 2 = ☐						
Half of 460						
320 ÷ 2 = ☐						
Half of 780						
☐ ÷ 2 = 70						
660 ÷ 2 = ☐						
980 ÷ 2 = ☐						
☐ ÷ 2 = 340						
Half of 500						

Read out the whole question.

Earn three consecutive ticks.

Use this space for your notes and working out.

$4 \times 9 = \square$	
$\square \times 5 = 45$	
$8 \times 3 = \square$	
$3 \times 7 = \square$	
$4 \times 8 = \square$	
$3 \times \square = 27$	
$4 \times 6 = \square$	
$3 \times 6 = \square$	

$45 \div 5 = \square$	
$24 \div 4 = \square$	
$9 \div 3 = \square$	
$24 \div 4 = \square$	
$35 \div 5 = \square$	
$21 \div \square = 7$	
$10 \div 2 = \square$	
$20 \div 5 = \square$	

Dividing by 10

Multiplying by 10

Use this space for your notes and working out.

Read out the whole statement.

Earn three consecutive ticks.

800 ÷ 10 = ☐					
1200 ÷ 10 = ☐					
1500 ÷ 10 = ☐					
☐ ÷ 10 = 50					
1100 ÷ 10 = ☐					
100 ÷ 10 = ☐					
☐ ÷ 10 = 90					
700 ÷ 10 = ☐					

10 x 94 = ☐					
10 x 30 = ☐					
12 x 10 = ☐					
☐ x 10 = 960					
10 x 50 = ☐					
79 x 10 = ☐					
☐ x 10 = 520					
33 x 10 = ☐					

Read out the whole sentence.

Use this space for your notes and working out.

Double 250						
320 x 2 = ☐						
90 x 2 = ☐						
2 x 120 = ☐						
Double 270						
Double 370						
190 x 2 = ☐						
410 x 2 = ☐						

Half of 700						
360 ÷ 2 = ☐						
Half of 560						
320 ÷ 2 = ☐						
Half of 780						
☐ ÷ 2 = 120						
680 ÷ 2 = ☐						
Half of 500						

Read out the whole question and earn three consecutive ticks

Use this space for your notes and working out.

Adding and subtracting pairs of multiples of 10

This section uses the skills you have already practised.

Look, if you know
42 + 29 = 71

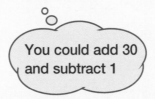

You could add 30 and subtract 1

Then you can use this to work out,
420 + **29**0 = **71**0

420 + 290 = ☐								
340 + 190 = ☐								
650 − 320 = ☐								
780 + 130 = ☐								
510 − 190 = ☐								
160 + 160 = ☐								
260 + 250 = ☐								
140 + 790 = ☐								
730 − 380 = ☐								
220 + 390 = ☐								
640 + 360 = ☐								
600 − 420 = ☐								
400 + 590 = ☐								

Decimals

Adding and subtracting ones and tenths

Ones Tenths

3.4

If you want to add
1.5 and 1.3

You can add the tenths
5 + 3 = 8

and then add the ones
1 + 1 = 2

So,   1.5 + 1.3 = 2.8

1.5 + 1.3 =	
1.2 + 2.3 =	
2.4 + 2.4 =	
3.4 + 4.5 =	
1.8 + 3.3 =	
4.7 + 1.2 =	
0.6 + 1.3 =	
1.5 − 0.6 =	
5.3 + 2.8 =	
2.4 − 1.3 =	
4.8 + 2.5 =	
3.2 + 3.9 =	
4.5 + 2.8 =	

Use this space for your notes and working out.

Mixed worded problems

These are worded problems.

Read the question and work out the answer using strategies you've learnt. Earn three consecutive ticks.

Use this space for your notes and working out.

Take 43 away from 64							
What is 17 added to 19?							
How much change do you get from £1 if you spend 36p?							
What is seven multiplied by four?							
What time is it 45 minutes after 6.30pm?							
It is 2.45pm. How many minutes is it until 3.15pm?							
How many minutes is it from 6.20pm to 7.10pm?							
How much change do you get from £1 if you spend 72p?							
What is 24 divided by 4?							

The language of fractions

Fractions are another way of writing decimals and percentages.

You need to know that $\frac{1}{5}$ is 'one fifth'. You can find $\frac{1}{5}$ by dividing by 5.

$\frac{1}{4}$ can be found by ÷ 4
$\frac{1}{2}$ can be found by ÷ 2
$\frac{1}{3}$ can be found by ÷ 3
$\frac{1}{10}$ can be found by ÷ 10

$\frac{1}{4}$ can be worked out by halving and halving again.

$\frac{1}{5}$ can be worked out by dividing by 10 and then doubling.

One half of 26							
One tenth of 50							
One third of 9							
One fifth of 15							
One quarter of 12							
$\frac{1}{10}$ of 150							
$\frac{1}{2}$ of 150							
$\frac{1}{2}$ of 18							
One tenth of 70							
$\frac{1}{5}$ of 25							
$\frac{1}{4}$ of 20							
One third of 21							
One half of 36							

Use this space for your notes and working out.

Page 150 started on: _ _ _ _ _ _ _ _ _ _ _ _

Page 150 finished on: _ _ _ _ _ _ _ _ _ _ _

Fractions and decimals

Use this space for your notes and working out.

Fractions and decimals are ways of representing numbers.

You need to know that

$0.5 = \frac{1}{2}$ $0.25 = \frac{1}{4}$

$0.2 = \frac{2}{10}$ $7.25 = 7\frac{1}{4}$

$\frac{9}{10} = 0.9$ $\frac{7}{10}$ is 0.7

Read out the number and then say the equivalent fraction or decimal.

$\frac{3}{10}$ you say "three tenths equals 0.3"

$\frac{3}{10}$							
0.5							
3.25							
$\frac{9}{10}$							
0.2							
$\frac{7}{10}$							
0.25							
$5\frac{1}{4}$							
0.1							
7.25							
0.4							
$\frac{1}{2}$							
0.3							

You need to read out the whole question.

Earn three consecutive ticks.

3 x 7 = ☐								
24 ÷ 6 = ☐								
9 x ☐ = 27								
40 ÷ ☐ = 8								
9 x 4 = ☐								
5 x ☐ = 35								
☐ x 7 = 70								
3 x ☐ = 18								
☐ x 2 = 18								
24 ÷ 4 = ☐								
5 x 9 = ☐								
21 ÷ 3 = ☐								
25 ÷ 5 = ☐								

Use this space for your notes and working out.

Square numbers

Use this space for your notes and working out.

These are numbers which are made by multiplying numbers by themselves.

For example,

$$2 \times 2 = 4$$
$$5 \times 5 = 25$$

They can also be written,

4^2 You need to say, "4 squared equals 16"

because, $4 \times 4 = 16$

2 x 2 = ☐							
5 x 5 = ☐							
7 x 7 = ☐							
9 x 9 = ☐							
4 x 4 = ☐							
8 x 8 = ☐							
3^2 = ☐							
6 x 6 = ☐							
1 x 1 = ☐							
7^2 = ☐							
10 x 10 = ☐							
9^2 = ☐							
8 x 8 = ☐							

Using doubles

You can use the doubles facts that you know to add 2 numbers which are close to each other. Here are some tips:

16 + 18 is double 18 and then subtract 2.

160 + 170 is double 16, add 1 and then multiply by 10

16 + 16 = 32
16 + 17 = 33
160 + 170 = 330

Double 19							
17 + 18 = ☐							
170 + 180 = ☐							
36 + 35 = ☐							
45 + 47 = ☐							
27 + 27 = ☐							
270 + 280 = ☐							
260 + 280 = ☐							
Double 37							
370 + 380 = ☐							
Double 135							
135 + 140 = ☐							
Double 65							

Use this space for your notes and working out.

Nearly numbers

Use this space for your notes and working out.

This page is about adding numbers with either 1 or 9 in the ones column.

Remember, a way to add 9, 19, 29 is to round it up to the nearest 10 and then subtract 1.

And a way to add 11, 21, 31, 41 is to round it down to the nearest 10 and then add 1.

$54 + 19 = \square$						
$31 + 146 = \square$						
$384 + 29 = \square$						
$67 + 69 = \square$						
$41 + 304 = \square$						
$99 + 52 = \square$						
$79 + 125 = \square$						
$496 + 11 = \square$						
$119 + 29 = \square$						
$71 + 368 = \square$						
$264 + 99 = \square$						
$21 + 85 = \square$						
$49 + 49 = \square$						

Multiplying and dividing

Multiplying and dividing by 6.

If you know your 3 times table, it can help you with your 6 times table.

Think about doubling numbers.

Look,
$3 \times 7 = 21$
$6 \times 7 = 42$

$3 \times 8 = 24$
$6 \times 8 = 48$

Read the whole question.

6 x 7 = ☐

6 x 2 = ☐

5 x 6 = ☐

6 x 6 = ☐

36 ÷ 6 = ☐

9 x 6 = ☐

24 ÷ 6 = ☐

6 x ☐ = 18

6 x ☐ = 60

42 ÷ 6 = ☐

6 x ☐ = 0

54 ÷ ☐ = 9

6 x 1 = ☐

Use this space for your notes and working out.

Use this space for your notes and working out.

Adding and subtracting 3-digit multiples of 10

If you need to add
        370 + 250
you can use the skills you already have.

For example,
        370 + **25**0
        37 + 25
        37 + **20** = 57
        57 + **3** + **2** = 62

So,   **37**0 + **25**0 = **62**0

Can you see how it was done?

370 + 250 = ☐							
450 + 260 = ☐							
190 + 420 = ☐							
520 − 280 = ☐							
210 − 150 = ☐							
670 + 140 = ☐							
760 − 480 = ☐							
460 + 360 = ☐							
190 + 190 = ☐							
630 − 390 = ☐							
570 + 180 = ☐							
550 − 270 = ☐							
230 + 240 = ☐							

Recap grid

Use these grids to fill in any work you have found difficult so far. Copy out the questions you found hard or write in your own questions.

Use this space for your notes and working out.

Pairs of decimals

Use this space for your notes and working out.

Pairs of decimals which make whole numbers.

These questions all involve decimals with ones and tenths.

Look at this example,

$3.7 + \square = 4$

You can count on in tenths ... 3.8 ... 3.9 ... 4.0

So, $3.7 + \boxed{0.3} = 4$

But also, you should know that $7 + 3 = 10$

> **You need to read the whole sum**

$3.7 + \square = 4$					
$5.2 + \square = 6$					
$0.4 + \square = 1$					
$6.1 + \square = 7$					
$4.4 - \square = 4$					
$7.5 + \square = 8$					
$1.2 - \square = 1$					
$3.3 + \square = 4$					
$\square + 4.6 = 5$					
$\square + 7.9 = 8$					
$8.8 + \square = 9$					
$5.5 - \square = 5$					
$1.5 + \square = 5$					

Subtracting 4-digit numbers

These 4-digit numbers are all either side of multiples of 1000.

For example,

$$3004 - 2997 = \square$$

$$2997 \xrightarrow{+3} 3000 \xrightarrow{+4} 3004$$

So, $3004 - 2997 = \boxed{7}$

This way is called bridging.

3004 - 2997 = ☐								
4005 - 3996 = ☐								
2002 - 1996 = ☐								
9003 - 8994 = ☐								
7008 - 6996 = ☐								
3004 - 1999 = ☐								
5003 - 3995 = ☐								
3004 - 1998 = ☐								
4001 - 3992 = ☐								
6007 - 5995 = ☐								
8002 - 6995 = ☐								
1007 - 994 = ☐								
3005 - 2999 = ☐								

Use this space for your notes and working out.

Multiplying by 10 and 100

Use this space for your notes and working out.

Multiplying by 10 and 100 is a really useful thing to do.

If you multiply by 10 the digits move one place to the left.

$39 \times 10 = 390$

If you multiply by 100 the digits move two places to the left.

$874 \times 100 = 87,400$

If you multiply by 10 numbers get **10 times bigger**

If you multiply by 100 numbers get **100 times bigger**

39 × 10 = ☐								
100 × 25 = ☐								
452 × 10 = ☐								
10 × 342 = ☐								
100 × 691 = ☐								
☐ × 34 = 340								
10 × 648 = ☐								
439 × 100 = ☐								
100 × 966 = ☐								
10 × ☐ = 270								
78 × 100 = ☐								
100 × 40 = ☐								
44 × 10 = ☐								

Dividing by 10 and 100

Dividing by 10 and 100 is the opposite of multiplying by 10 and 100.

The numbers get smaller.

The digits move one or two places to the right.

Look,

$$5000 \div 10 = 500$$

$$2300 \div 100 = 23$$

$3000 \div 10 = \square$								
$9000 \div 100 = \square$								
$8300 \div 10 = \square$								
$5400 \div 100 = \square$								
$240 \div 10 = \square$								
$190 \div 10 = \square$								
$450 \div 10 = \square$								
$6800 \div 10 = \square$								
$7200 \div 100 = \square$								
$300 \div 100 = \square$								
$7800 \div 100 = \square$								
$3100 \div 100 = \square$								
$6000 \div 10 = \square$								

Use this space for your notes and working out.

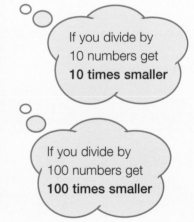

If you divide by 10 numbers get **10 times smaller**

If you divide by 100 numbers get **100 times smaller**

Time

Use this space for your notes and working out.

Time is a very important area for using numbers.

You'll need to be able to work out how long it is between times and also know some facts about time. You need to read these sentences and fill in the missing word or number.

7 o'clock add one hour is ...	
1.15am to 1.50am is ... minutes	
2 years is ... months	
7.30pm to 8.05pm is ... minutes	
8.45am to 9.45am is ... minutes	
2 days is ... hours	
2.25am to 3.00am is ... minutes	
35 minutes before 4.00pm is ...	
5.25pm to 6.30pm is ... minutes	

It's good to say how you worked it out

Congratulations!

You have now completed Power of 2

We welcome any
comments you may have.
www.123learning.co.uk